tell me a

RAMAYANA

Ritika Sabbharwal

Nita Mehta™
WISKIDZ
ENRICHING YOUNG MINDS

An Imprint of Nita Mehta Publications

Contents

Narada Meets Valmiki

Long ago, there lived a Sage by the name of Valmiki. One day as he sat thinking if there was an ideal man, Saint Narada came to his ashram. After welcoming him, Valmiki asked, "O, all-knowing Narada, tell me is there a man larger than life, yet human in all the three worlds? Who has human qualities that others do not possess?"

"Yes, there is," replied Narada without hesitation.

Narada's face lit up as he spoke,

"He is Rama of Ayodhya. His character speaks of more virtues that one can imagine, and he protects the weak while destroying evil."

Narada then narrated to Valmiki the story of Rama. Valmiki was so impressed with the story that he pondered over it, even after Narada had left.

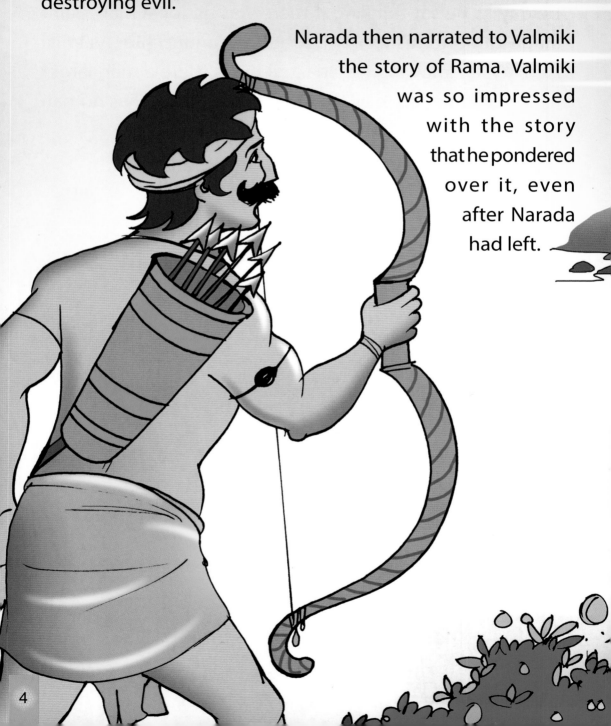

As he was walking with these thoughts brimming in his head, he happened to see a pair of mating birds. But suddenly, there was a cry of pain. A hunter's arrow had pierced through the heart of the male bird and the female let out an intense cry.

As Valmiki cursed the hunter, he was at once filled with a sense of remorse and let out his feelings through poetry.

He sat to meditate and as he did so, Lord Brahma appeared bestowing upon him the power and the vision to write the story of Rama. As Valmiki spoke a verse to the God, Lord Brahma blessed him saying, "Let your words grow into poetry such that it will be remembered for generations to come."

As the meditation ended, Valmiki and his disciples repeated the verse again and again till it was entrenched in their minds. Valmiki then composed the story of Rama, the Ramayana, which to this day has not been forgotten and is told the world over.

Rama is born

Many years ago there was a kingdom named Kosala, on the banks of the Sarayu, a river to the north of the holy Ganga. The kingdom was rich and prosperous and its capital Ayodhya was the lifeline of the entire kingdom. It was ruled by King Dashratha, a wise and just ruler who was helped by his council of experienced ministers and family priests.

Even though Dashratha had attained glory, fame and prosperity he was not a happy man. He forever questioned who would succeed him, for he had no sons. And while being happily married for many years to his three wives, Kausalya, Sumitra and Kaikeyi, he had not been blessed with a son. The King was advised by his priests to perform a special sacrifice. This was the *Putrakameshti*, prescribed for having a son.

While the arrangements for the ritual took place, there was something brewing in the heavens. Vishnu, the Preserver had chosen Dashratha to father four sons, each of whom would be a part of Lord Vishnu. This was all part of a plan made in heaven, which would be revealed later.

During the yagna, as the ghee was poured into the fire, from the flames rose a creature with a resplendent glowing face, holding a golden pot full of *paayasam* (sweetened milk and rice).

"I come from the Creator," he said to Dashratha, "to give you this *paayasam* for your wives. Feed it to them and they will be blessed with sons, heirs of the kingdom of Kosala."

Dashratha accepted the vessel and distributed the paayasam to his three wives, giving a portion each to Kausalya, Sumitra and Kaikeyi, and a second and last helping to Sumitra. His wives happiness knew no bounds, and soon they were all expectant mothers.

Vishwamitra's Request

In course of time, they gave birth to four sons. Kausalya bore the eldest, Rama while Kaikeyi gave birth to Bharata. Sumitra gave birth to twins, Lakshmana and Shatrughna, having consumed the divine *paayasam* twice. The kingdom rejoiced as the four princes were born. As they grew, they showed remarkable characteristics. Rama was responsible and believed in truth and justice. He was born a leader of men and was loved tremendously by his brothers. Bharata was noble and obedient; Lakshmana was firm and impulsive while Shatrughna was kind and gentle.

They studied the Vedas, were instructed in archery and martial arts, imbibing all the princely qualities. All of them grew up to be learned, virtuous, righteous and brave men. Rama and Lakshmana were especially devoted to each other, as were Bharata and Shatrughna. Before long, the brothers had matured and King Dasharatha began to dream of good brides for his sons. While the King planned the future of his sons, the great Sage Vishwamitra arrived in Ayodhya wanting to meet the King.

"It seems clear that he has a mission and a serious one at that," thought Dasharatha to himself as he welcomed the Sage.

"I am blessed indeed, learned Vishwamitra that you have graced my court and I will be honoured to be of service. Is there anything in my power that I can do for you? If so, command and I shall obey," said King Dasharatha.

This is exactly what the Sage had hoped.

"O King, I have come here with a special purpose. I am engaged in performing a sacrifice at my *ashram* but every time it nears completion, two powerful demons Maricha and Subahu ruin it by throwing unclean blood and flesh on the sacred fire."

Dashratha looked apprehensively at the Sage as he continued. "I could destroy the demons but because of the spiritual path that I have undertaken I am not allowed to show anger, let alone curse them. My troubles will end only if you send Rama to help me in getting rid of these beasts."

The King trembled at the idea of allowing his son to go fight demons. He thought that Rama wasn't prepared. Despairingly, he said,

"Rama is not even sixteen, how can he fight demons? It is not right to send such a young boy to help you, but I can send my entire army to assist you. What is more, I will even accompany you along with them."

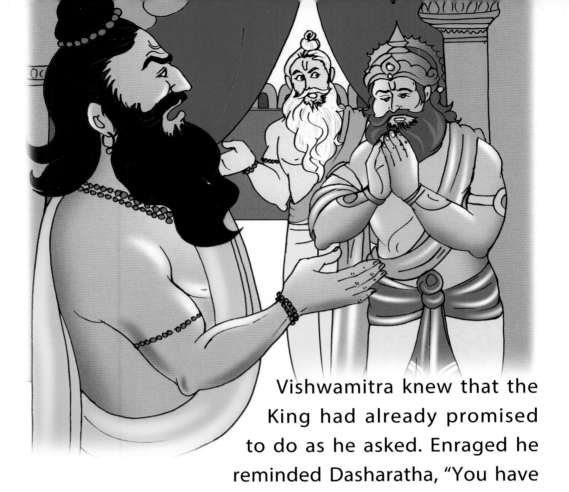

Vishwamitra knew that the King had already promised to do as he asked. Enraged he reminded Dasharatha, "You have already given your word to me. How can a king whose dynasty boasts of honesty and truth waver to act on his word? Remember, that such an act will dishonour your family. This conduct is unworthy of your lineage!"

Vasishtha, an advisor and priest of the King intervened, "Gracious King, do as Vishwamitra says. He is the bravest and wisest of all. Rama will be safe. With his powers and weapons, he will shield and preserve your son."

Listening to the wise Vasishtha, better sense dawned on Dasharatha and he consented. Rama and Lakshmana, inseparable companions, left together with the Sage.

Slaying Demons

As Rama, Lakshmana and Vishwamitra walked on the bank of the Sarayu, Vishwamitra stopped and spoke to both of them. "It is here that I will give you your first weapons, Bala and Atibala.

With these you will feel no hunger, thirst, fatigue or fever."
Rama and Lakshmana felt a gush of energy enter their body
as they absorbed the powers bestowed upon them. The three
then resumed their journey. Through their journey Vishwamitra
related stories and events that enlightened the Princes.
Soon, they reached the point where the Sarayu crossed its path
with the great Ganga and paid their respect. Across the river,
they approached a dense but deserted
forest. "This," Vishwamitra said, "is
the Dandaka forest. It was once an
inhabited country blessed by Lord
Indra. The people lived happily till
Tataka, having the
strength of

a thousand
elephants along
with her son Maricha, brought
havoc to the place. The great
Sage Agastya had killed
Tataka's husband with a curse
which threw her into a rage.
She rushed at the Sage and
he cursed her to remain a
demoness and her son a
demon for life."

Vishwamitra thus set the first task for
both the Princes-to get rid of Tataka.
Rama shot an arrow into the forest
sky as a warning of impending disaster.
The moment he did, Tataka attacked the two
Princes, throwing stones and rocks at them.
The hideous and massive demoness wearing a garland
of human bones around her neck, charged at them, baring her
sharp claws as she growled at Rama. Swift in her movement,
Tataka sprang from one place to another. Rama quickly cut off
her hands, nose and ears and finally let loose an arrow which
pierced her heart as she fell to the ground.

Extremely pleased with Rama's performance, Vishwamitra said, "Do not regret killing a woman, for even though you think this goes against your Kshatriya upbringing, this situation needed such an action. It was for protection and not for causing destruction that you did so."

Early next morning after their prayers, Vishwamitra gave Rama the entire range of divine weapons, bestowing upon him the Dharmachakra, Kalachakra and Dandachakra which were the wheels of Righteousness (Dharma), Time (Kaal) and Punishment (Danda). He also conferred upon him Vishnu's discus, the Sudarshana and Indra's thunderbolt, Vajra along with other divine weapons. As they proceeded, Rama pointed to a hill with a lovely forest and asked Vishwamitra, "Is that the place we are headed? Is it your ashram?" Vishwamitra replied. "Yes, it is known as Siddhashrama. This is where Lord Vishnu's dwarf incarnation came to earth."

Once they reached there, Rama asked Vishwamitra to start his rites without any delay. Five days and nights passed quietly as the Sage had taken the vow of silence. On the sixth day the skies were dark and gloomy.

"Maricha and Subahu are coming," said the brothers in unison even as the Sage continued his vow of silence.

As the sacrificial fire rose, Rama looked up to see the demons preparing to shower unclean things on the sacrificial fire. Rama moved with the speed of lightening and severely wounded Maricha as he was hurled hundred of miles away into the sea. He killed Subahu and their army of followers were chased and destroyed till the sky shone with sunlight.

Rid of the menace of the demons, the rituals were performed in a calm and clean environment. Siddhashrama was restored to its prior glory.

As the Princes looked towards Vishwamitra for orders, the ascetics of the ashram informed him,

"A sacrifice has begun in Mithila in the kingdom of Videha, started by King Janaka where the main attraction is a bow owned by Lord Shiva."

Vishwamitra added, "Many princes and kings have tried to lift and draw that bow but all have failed till now. The bow is the test of strength for Janaka's daughter Sita's future husband." Rama felt a sense of anticipation as they moved on, towards Mithila.

The Marriage of Rama & Sita

In a few days, they reached the outskirts of Mithila where people had started to gather for King Janaka's twelve day sacrifice. Hearing of the Sage's presence in his kingdom, King Janaka came to greet him. Curious about the two Princes, the King asked many questions to which Vishwamitra told him about their victories and the reason they were there. The next day when they arrived at the ceremony, Vishwamitra came straight to the point and asked the King to let them see the bow of Shiva.

As Janaka sent for the bow, he narrated its history to the Princes. "This bow belongs to Shiva Mahadeva. During his father-in-law's sacrifice, Shiva was disregarded, neglected and insulted. The Gods had been a silent witness to his humiliation. Enraged, Shiva drew his bow towards them and prepared to destroy them. They pleaded for mercy and Shiva then handed the bow over to them. They in turn gave it to my ancestors and since then it has been a family heirloom, protected and worshipped by all," concluded Janaka.

He also recounted how his daughter had come to him through strange events. Once King Janaka was performing a yagna and while he began to plough the earth as a ritual preparation for the sacrificial site, he came upon a child behind some bushes. He named this girl Sita and brought her home to be his own, as he was childless and regarded her as a gift from Mother Earth. Continuing in a concerned tone he added, "Sita's marriage is no easy task as the man who is to wed my daughter should be able to draw this mighty bow and has to earn her hand in marriage with unchallenged valour. There are no exceptions."

Rama and Lakshmana listened with great interest. Many princes had come earlier trying in vain to lift the bow and returned defeated. Janaka's men brought the bow which was kept in a safe iron box, on an eight wheeled cart drawn by five hundred strong men.

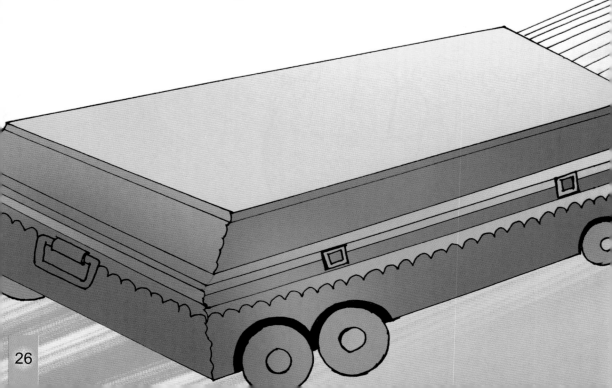

"Here," said Janaka, "is the bow worshipped through generations. Let Rama see this bow." Rama came forth and examined it. Many before Rama had tried to lift the bow but none could succeed. It created terror amongst cowards and for the selfish it was unapproachable. Rama stood with his head bowed, prayed silently and asked permission from Janaka and Vishwamitra to raise the bow and try to bend it.

As they nodded their assent, Rama, to their amazement bent down and lifted the formidable bow and then to their utter astonishment, snapped it into two. The court was filled with shouts of "Victory to Rama, glory to Rama!"

Janaka proclaimed, "My beloved daughter Sita is to be wedded to this Prince." Messengers were then sent to Ayodhya to give the news to Dashratha and invite him to this kingdom. When King Dashratha came to Mithila, he and King Janaka discussed the matter of brides for Rama's three younger brothers. Janaka's younger daughter Urmila was married to Lakshmana.

Janaka's younger brother, Kushadhwaja also had two daughters, Mandavi and Shrutakirti who were then married to Bharata and Shatrughna respectively.

After the wedding, Sage Vishwamitra left for the Himalayas, while King Dasharatha, his four sons and their brides along with their royal entourage left for Ayodhya.

Parashurama

On their way to Ayodhya, the royal entourage was rudely interrupted by a storm, from which emerged Parashurama. He was the sworn enemy of the *Kshatriyas*, and stood with a bow and quiver on one shoulder and his famous battle axe on the other. Parashurama had circled the earth several times killing many Kshatriyas, as one person belonging to that race had killed his father, Jamadgani.

Towering in front of Rama, he declared, "There are only two divine bows, both designed by the divine architect Vishwakarma in this world. You have managed to break one belonging to Lord Shiva. Here is the other, belonging to Lord Vishnu. If you are able to string it then you will be worthy of battle against me."

Dashratha tried to convince Parashurama by reminding him that he was a Brahmin and thereby such acts would only demean him. Unperturbed, Parashurama remained focused on Rama and mockingly asked if he was ready. Rama taking the bow and arrow from Parashurama drew the string and pointing it straight at him, said,

"I shall take all the powers you have attained through your penance," said Rama sternly. Parashurama shrank till Rama's level and asked him to only leave him with the power to move so that he could be able to reach his home, in the Mahendra range. Rama sent the arrow flying and the gloom that surrounded them vanished as the sun shone upon them with its majestic rays.

Rama and Sita lived in Ayodhya for many years, till one day King Dasharatha decided that he would pronounce Rama as his successor to the throne. The entire kingdom was overjoyed and began the preparations for the coronation. During this time, Bharata and Shatrughna were not in the kingdom and were visiting Bharata's maternal grandfather, while Lakshmana remained besides Rama during this happy occasion.

The Wicked Plot

While the entire kingdom rejoiced hearing the news, there was one corner of the palace where this news caused a different reaction. Manthara, a hunched back maidservant of Queen Kaikeyi was shocked and angered on hearing the news of Rama's coronation. She rushed to Kaikeyi. "How can you rest when a flood of misfortunes comes your way? You have been betrayed. These events are conjured so that you cannot protest," said Manthara to the queen. Kaikeyi taken aback by Manthara's outburst said, "But that is good news. It has been the tradition that the eldest son becomes the heir to the throne. I am happy for Rama." Manthara tried convincing the queen that great injustice had been done to her and to her son.

She said, "Bharata is the right successor to the throne and if Rama becomes the King then you and your son would be looked at as mere servants."

Manthara further poisoned Kaikeyi's mind by telling her that she was at present the King's favourite Queen but when Rama would become the King, the tables would turn and Kausalya would then take her place. She finally added, "Since Bharata is not even here to protect his rights, his fate rests in the hands of others."

Kaikeyi had a grave expression on her face. This last effort from Manthara had worked. "What can I do about it?" asked Kaikeyi. "Long ago," she reminded Kaikeyi, "during the battle in which you accompanied your husband, you saved his life risking your own. He had then offered you two boons which you said you would use later when you required."

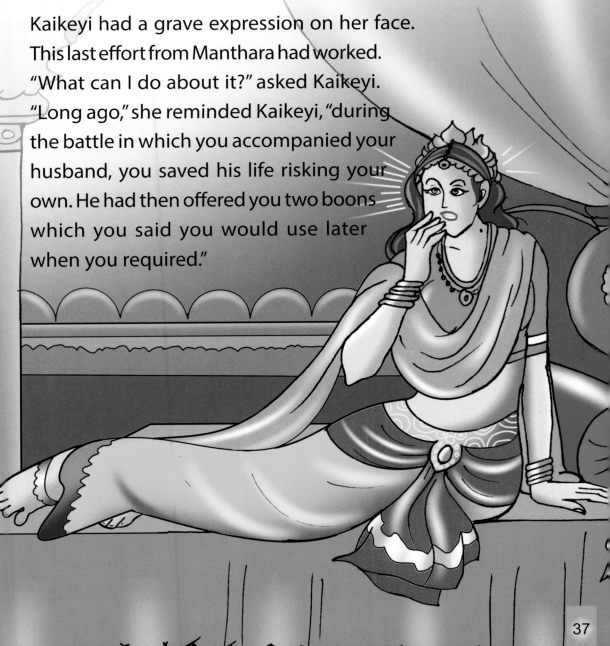

Kaikeyi remembered the incident and the promise. "Well," said Manthara, "that day has come when you can ask for your boons. As the first boon you ask for Rama to be exiled for fourteen years and the second, coronation of your son, Bharata."

After making all the arrangements for the coronation, King Dasharatha proceeded to Kaikeyi to tell her the good news. As he entered her chamber he saw her distraught face and asked her what was wrong. "I have a wish that I need you to fulfil," she said. "I will do anything to take your distress away. I swear by Rama that I will fulfil what you desire," replied Dasharatha. Overjoyed that he had sworn on Rama, Kaikeyi knew that he would not go back on his word. She then proceeded to tell him, "Do you remember that once in a battle I had saved your life and you had granted me two boons? I feel now the time has come to ask them." Dasharatha asked her to spell out her two wishes. Asking all the Gods to bear witness to what the King had consented to, she continued, "I ask that my son Bharata be coronated king. With the second boon I ask that Rama be exiled to the forest for fourteen years."

Dasharatha was shocked beyond words. "Rama, be banished for fourteen years!" he repeated to himself. He pleaded her to take back her boons but to no avail. She threatened to kill herself if her wishes were not fulfilled. Dasharatha, said in a hurtful tone, "I hereby do not consider you my wife nor do I consider your son to be mine. But what you ask shall be done."

The next morning when Rama heard that King Dasharatha lay unwell in Queen Kaikeyi's chambers, he rushed to see him. Dasharatha was inconsolable and due to his weak condition, was unable to speak. Kaikeyi then told Rama about her two demands.

Rama felt hurt that the King had not informed him personally, but agreed to the promise made by the King to Kaikeyi and after asking her to send for Bharata, left for his chambers to get his belongings.

Rama went to his mother, Kausalya and narrated the entire incident. She was shocked but understood that Rama had to obey the promise made by his father. And even though Lakshmana was furious, he and Sita decided to leave with Rama for the forest. The people of Ayodhya lay grief stricken on hearing the news of Rama's banishment. The three of them walked towards Dasharatha's palace for their final farewell. They met with King Dasharatha as all the people in the palace looked on and bade them farewell even though the King insisted that Rama stay back and rule the kingdom.

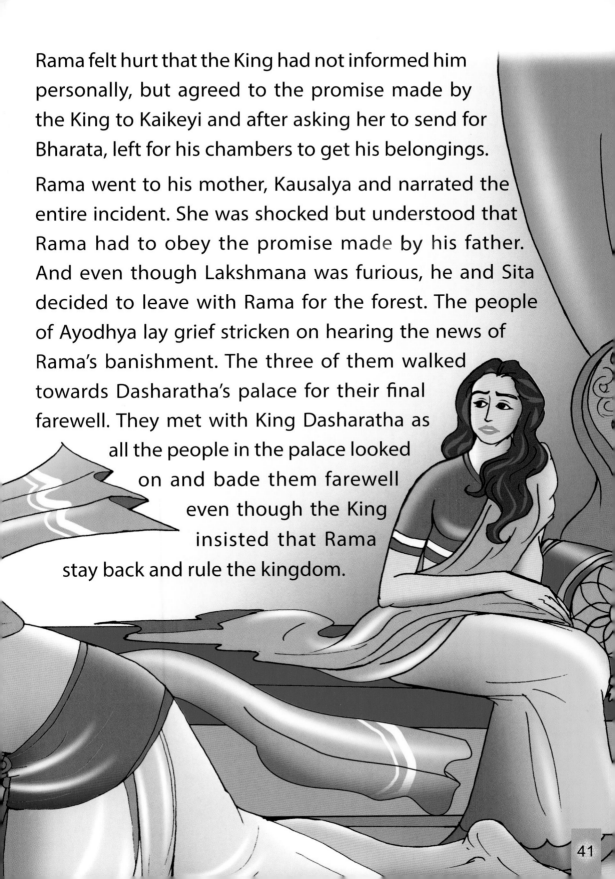

Kaikeyi handed them the robes made of bark which they were to wear for their journey, leaving all their worldly possessions behind. Dasharatha ordered his loyal minister and charioteer Sumantra to drive them to the edge of the forest. As they entered the forest, the three headed towards the Chitrakuta mountain, far away from Ayodhya.

Bharata Returns

After Rama left, the King remained bed ridden. He told Kausalya that he was paying for his past mistakes and narrated the incident that happened one fateful day when he was hunting near the banks of the river Sarayu.

"One day I thought I heard a sound by the river. Since I had been trained to hit a target in the direction from which its sound was coming without even having to look at it, I shot in that direction and suddenly heard a human crying. I rushed to the site, only to see a young ascetic named Shravana. He had come to fetch water for his blind parents and was their sole support and I killed him.

I went to his parents and gave them the tragic news. They cursed me saying that I would one day grieve for my son till the point of death and setting alight their own funeral pyre, they died."

He told her that the curse was taking its effect now and that he could feel his end would come soon. The next morning Kausalya and Sumitra woke up to see that their husband had passed away during the night.

The whole kingdom of Ayodhya mourned. Bharata and Shatrughna were then called back in order to conduct the funeral rites for the King. The day messengers were sent to bring Bharata, he had a bad dream which made him very anxious and uneasy. The messengers told him that an urgent matter awaited him in Ayodhya. Approaching Ayodhya he prayed that everything was fine. But as they entered he sensed as if the kingdom was in mourning. Not finding Dasharatha, he quickly went to his mother Kaikeyi and asked where his father was.

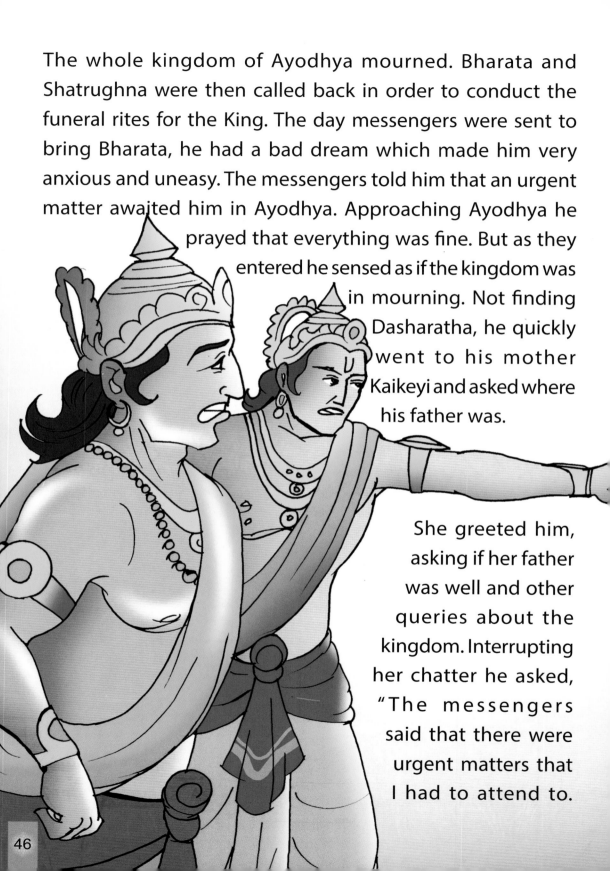

She greeted him, asking if her father was well and other queries about the kingdom. Interrupting her chatter he asked, "The messengers said that there were urgent matters that I had to attend to.

What are they? Where is my father and why does our kingdom look so sorrowful?" Kaikeyi had to break the news. She casually told him about his father's death, the two boons and Rama's exile, stating that she had done all for his well being. Hearing this, Bharata fell to the floor, wailing in despair for his father's death. Kaikeyi sternly told him to stand up and stop grieving as he would now be in charge of an entire kingdom. Flabbergasted, Bharata accused his mother of killing her own husband and refused to identify her as his mother.

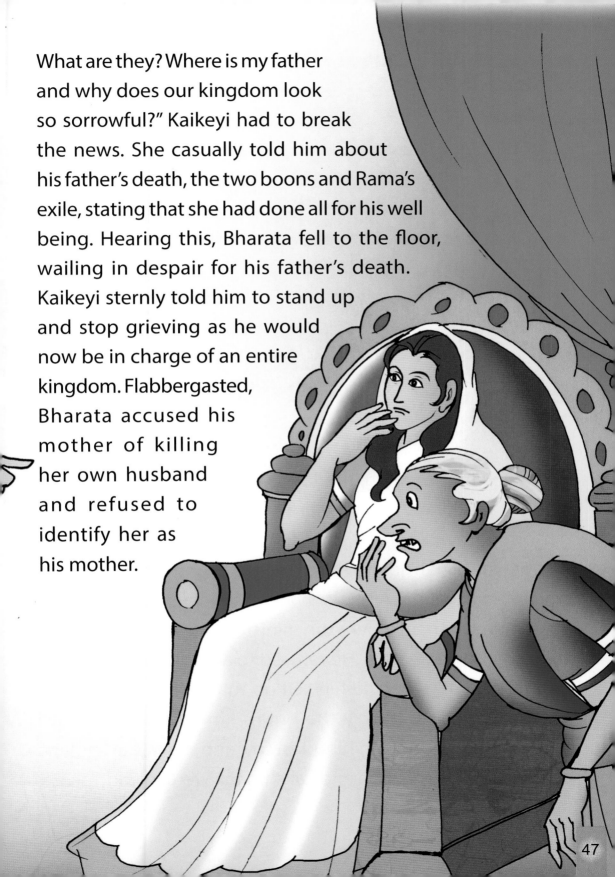

The Brothers Meet

The following morning, the last rites for the King's funeral were performed by Bharata. As the funeral drew to a close, both Bharata and Shatrughna sat brooding over the tragic events which had occurred. After the twelve-day period of mourning, a meeting was held where the ministers announced the new successor to be Bharata. He refused to accept the throne and told them that he would himself go to Chitrakuta and bring his brother back. Nearly the entire kingdom of Ayodhya accompanied Bharata in his quest to bring Rama, Lakshmana and Sita back. Rama Sita and Lakshmana were leading a very happy life in Chitrakuta.

One day, while sitting with Sita, Rama heard sounds of commotion and asked Lakshmana to see what it was. Angered and having jumped to the worst conclusion, Lakshmana told Rama that Bharata had come with an army to kill him.

"Bharata would never do such a thing," said Rama calmly.

Ordering the army to halt, Bharata set out on foot with Shatrughna towards Rama's abode. As he approached a hut, he looked inside and saw Rama sitting with Sita and Lakshmana besides him. As their eyes met, Bharata filled with anguish, fell at Rama's feet sobbing like a lost child. Shatrughna too wept, overwhelmed by the sight of his elder brother reduced to living in a forest hut. Rama asked Bharata if the King was well and how Bharata was handling the affairs of the kingdom. Rama finally asked, "Why have you come?"

Bharata despondently replied, "O Rama, our father is dead, killed by the woman he loved, my mother, in her greed for power.

He could not survive your banishment. I returned only to find him gone. And they ask me to sit on the throne of Ayodhya which is rightfully yours. You must come back to Ayodhya. We need you and want you back." Rama told Bharata that he had to obey his father's words therefore could not leave with them. "My father died, waiting for me and I was not even there to perform his last rites," said a grief stricken Rama to Bharata on hearing of his beloved father's death.

Bharata, Shatrughna and Lakshmana raised him, then went to the banks of river Mandakini. Filling his cupped palms with water, Rama offered it to his dead father. Having performed the rites, they returned to Rama's hut. They parted for the night and the next morning Bharata asked his brother once again to reconsider and return to Ayodhya. When Rama declined, Bharata asked Rama to give his sandals to him. "Step on them so that your presence is forever felt. I shall place them on the throne and serve them faithfully till you return. And I will wait for you not a single day more than fourteen years or I will die if you shall delay," said Bharata.

After Rama stood on the sandals, Bharata accepted them and put them on his head. He declared that he would wear bark robes like his brother and rule under the shadow of his feet.

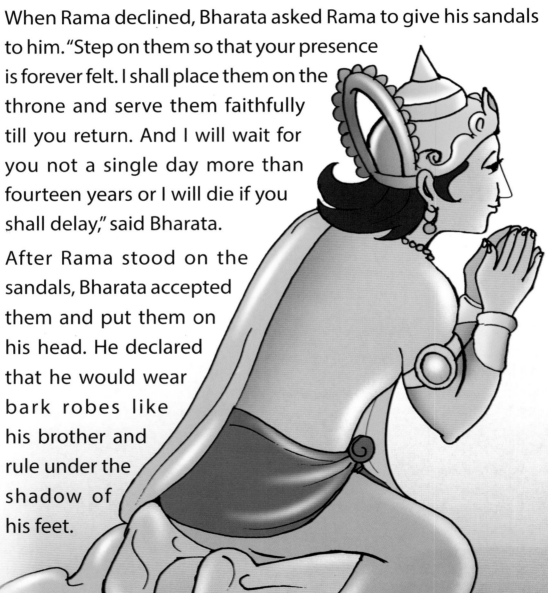

On returning, the Queens settled back into the palace, whereas Bharata moved to Nandigrama, a village outside Ayodhya. Rama's sandals were taken there in a royal ceremony and enthroned.

Meeting with Demons

As Bharata went back to Ayodhya, Rama along with Sita and Lakshmana proceeded to move further into the forest. For twelve years, they wandered through the forests, saw many great sights and killed many demons and wicked people.

In the thirteenth year of their exile, they reached a place called Panchavati in South India.

On their way to Panchavati, they came across a giant vulture. Not sure if it was a demon, the brothers asked aggressively,

"Who are you?"

The bird softly replied, "I am Jatayu, a friend of your father. I will watch over Sita and protect you through your stay in the jungle, if you allow me to do so." Rama consented and then the four of them were on their way to Panchavati, which was to be their humble abode till the end of their exile.

Shurpanakha

During their stay in Panchavati, one day Rama sat chanting his scriptures. A female demon happened to see him and was enchanted by him.

Disguising as a beautiful girl, she approached Rama and asked, "Who are you? And why are you in a forest ruled by demons?" "I am Rama, son of Dasharatha. I am here with my brother Lakshmana and wife Sita to fulfill a vow. And who are you?"

"I am Shurpanakha, sister of Ravana, demon-king of Lanka. I want to be your wife," she declared. She told him to leave Sita and come with her. Rama in a mischievous mood told her to ask his brother Lakshmana to marry her.

Easily swayed, Shurpanakha approached Lakshmana who went along with the game which Rama had started and said, "I do not think that you would like to be a wife of a slave, for I am my brother's slave. Rama will give up his wife with a little persuasion. Why don't you ask him again?"

This angered Shurpanakha and she assumed her true form of a demoness. She looked terrifying and Sita became afraid on seeing her. Shurpanakha glared at Sita and said, "I will kill you and then Rama can marry me."

Rama ended the mischief and told Lakshmana, "Do not kill her but just disfigure her so that she goes away."

Lakshmana then cut off Shurpanakha's nose and ears and let her go. She ran to her brother Khara in Janasthana and told him the entire story. But being a devious demoness she conveniently forgot to mention that it was she who had provoked them.

She also declared that she would only be happy if she would drink their blood. Khara sent his fourteen best demons to go after those who had harmed his sister. The demons attacked Rama and Lakshmana with their spears, only to be broken by Rama's arrows. The battle didn't last long, as they fell like trees having been so easily cut by the woodcutter's axe. On hearing of his fourteen demons being slained by Rama, Khara along with Trishira, the leader of his army and fourteen thousand demons went to fight against Rama.

The army raged at Rama, but he relentlessly let out his arrows as the enemy was no match for him. Having seen Rama vanquish his entire army of fourteen thousand demons, Trishira went striding towards Rama, wanting to avenge their death. This three headed demon pelted Ram with all his weapons, but soon all three heads were severed by Rama's flaming arrows.

Seeing his army and its commander slain, Khara was fearful but he too rushed to attack Rama with a mace in his hand. He hurled his magic mace which turned everything that came in its way to ashes, but Rama destroyed the mace and it fell down with a crash. He finally let loose a powerful arrow which struck Khara in the heart, putting him to death. The Gods rejoiced and applauded Rama for his victory as it signalled the beginning of the end of the reign of terror by these demons.

The Golden Deer

One of Ravana's messengers managed to escape and reported to his king how Rama had single-handedly killed his brother and crushed his entire army. Furious, Ravana decided to go to battle with Rama. The messenger advised Ravana that in direct battle he would lose to Rama as he was as powerful as the Gods for he was blessed with divine weapons.

"My Lord, there is another way that one can conquer Rama. He has a beautiful wife named Sita. If he was separated from her, he would be devastated, as he cannot live without her," said the scheming messenger. Ravana agreed with the messenger and set out to meet the demon Maricha, who had the ability to change his form. "Rama has killed my brother. I want to take revenge for my brother's death and need your help to take Sita away from him," said Ravana to Maricha.

This will lead to your devastation

Maricha was taken aback. Having once escaped death after being attacked by Rama, he had no intention of reliving that moment again. "Who has put this idea into your head? Rama remains undefeated and raising his fury by taking away Sita will only lead to your devastation. Sita is Rama's and Rama's alone, stop dreaming of possessing her," advised Maricha.

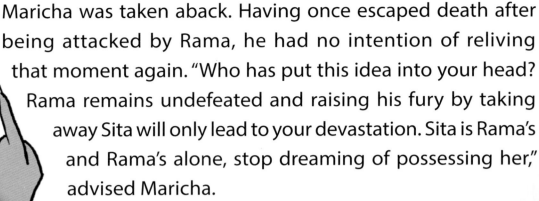

Maricha had been so convincing that Ravana began to have second thoughts and returned to his kingdom. By then Shurpanakha had heard of the humiliating fate her brother had faced. She went to Lanka, to talk to her brother Ravana. On her arrival she went straight to Ravana and asked him how he could sit on his throne without avenging his brother's murder. Ravana could not ignore her sentiments and asked, "Who is this Rama? What is his purpose here? Tell me!"

Shurpanakha deviously told him about Rama and his valour and then spoke about Sita's beauty. Hearing about Sita, Ravana's desires were aroused. Seeing his expression, Shurpanakha added, "In fact I wanted to get her for you, for I think that she would befit being your Queen and would adorn your palace."

There was no stopping Ravana now. He had to bring Sita. Shurpanakha's ploy had worked. Ravana went back to Maricha, but this time he wouldn't hear no for an answer. Ravana and Maricha arrived at Panchavati where they put their plan in motion. Maricha assumed the form of an enchanting golden deer, speckled with silver.

Seeing imaginably the most beautiful deer, Sita was captivated by it.

She saw it prance about near their hut, as she gathered flowers. She called out to Rama and Lakshmana, "Please come quickly. I've seen a wonderful deer, none like I've ever seen. Please catch it alive. It will look so serene in the gardens of Ayodhya."

Lakshmana was wary of the deer. "I think this is an illusion. It must be the demon Maricha who has changed its form," he declared. Sita would not listen. "I must have it, and if you can't bring it back alive, the skin will make a lovely spread."

"Who wouldn't like to possess such a fine animal?" said Rama and added, "And if it is Maricha, then he has been spared twice by me. This time he will not be that fortunate. Watch over Sita, Lakshmana. Don't leave her till I return. Jatayu is here as well. Guard her with your life."

Rama instructed Lakshmana before leaving to catch the deer. The deer kept prancing about and after some time, Rama, tired of the chase, took out one of his deadly arrows and aimed at the animal. It instantly fell to the ground.

But lo! The golden form vanished into thin air and in front of him was Maricha. But as he took his last breath, he spoke out in Rama's voice, "O Sita, O Lakshmana," and died. Rama was frantic. He knew that his call would be heard and that Sita was in danger. He only hoped that Lakshmana would not leave her side till he returned. Hearing the cry, Sita too became worried. She urged Lakshmana to go help his brother. He refrained. Fear and anger made Sita speak nasty words to Lakshmana.

"Are you not going because Rama is your stepbrother? All your love and respect for Rama is pretence. If you do not go right away, I will kill myself."

Lakshmana could not bear the pain of the words that Sita had inflicted on him and therefore, unwillingly, left her side in search of Rama. Before leaving, Lakshmana drew a circular line (Lakshmana-Rekha) around the house and told Sita that whatever happens, she should not cross that line because while she remains within it she is protected by God. Ravana meanwhile was waiting dressed as a holy mendicant hiding near the hut. As soon as Lakshmana left, he approached Sita and asked what she was doing there alone? She went into the hut to get food and water for the traveller and asked him to make himself at home.

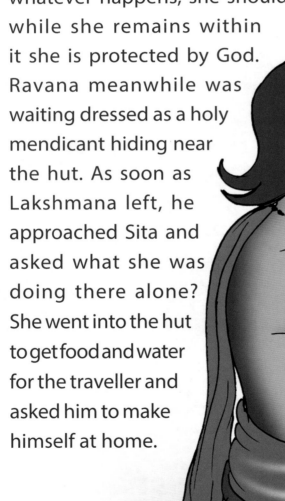

As soon as she entered the hut, Ravana ran behind her only to be obstructed by the Lakshmana-Rekha. Realizing its power, he sat a few steps away from the line knowing that he could not cross it. When she came out with the food, she asked him to take it from her hands as she could not move out of that circle.

Ravana then appeared to be disgruntled and told her that he wouldn't accept anything from someone who did not have the decency to serve him herself. Ashamed that an ascetic should return empty handed from her door, she crossed the line.

But as soon as she did, Ravana showed his true form and snatching her, put her in his flying chariot.

Seeing Jatayu perched on a tree, Sita called out, "I know you cannot fight this demon, but tell Rama that I was taken by force." Jatayu woke up and rose towards the chariot. He managed to break it and Ravana along with Sita was plunged back to earth. In his fury, Ravana chopped of Jatayu's wings and feet and flew towards Lanka, grasping Sita by her hair. On the way to Lanka, some monkeys seated on a mountain saw Sita throwing her ornaments down to earth. As they arrived in Lanka, Ravana asked Sita to marry him. Declining, she threatened Ravana that Rama would come for her and that he would never survive Rama's wrath. Ravana gave her a year to think over his proposal and if she declined, he would kill her.

Rama's Search

Mid way to his hut, Rama met Lakshmana and angrily asked him why he had disobeyed him and left Sita alone. Lakshmana then told him of Sita hearing his cry and then threatening to kill herself if he would not go in search for Rama.

Approaching the hut, they felt the silence of the forest around them and feared the worst. Sita was nowhere to be seen. Infuriated, Rama was on the verge of taking out all his weapons declaring that if Sita would not be returned to him, he would be the destroyer of all life that day.

Lakshmana calmed him down saying, "Brother, I know that you are hurt but how does killing all for the sin of one solve anything. Let us be calm and composed and look for Sita."

Moving further through the forest, they found a trail of Sita's footsteps and large ones besides them. They now knew that there was a powerful demon which had taken Sita away or worse, killed her. Soon, they saw Jatayu lying on the ground, in a pool of blood. In a soft sombre voice he told Rama that he tried his best to save Sita, but was too old and feeble compared to the demon Ravana.

He told them that she was alive and had been taken away by the demon. Saying this he finally breathed his last.

Rama and Lakshmana performed his last rites and then set out to find Sita. On crossing Janasthana, near the holy hermitage of Matanga they met a demon. They were seized by the monster with no legs or head, but two huge long arms and a mouth in the stomach area with long pointed teeth.

In its chest it had one large eye. Rama and Lakshmana struggled and realized his strength lay in his arms. They sliced them off and once the demon released them, he cried out, "I am Kabandha and I was meant to meet you so that you could deliver me from my curse. Please light my funeral pyre and then I will tell you about someone who can lead you to Sita." As the pyre was lit, a heavenly being arose from the fire saying, "Go West till you reach Lake Pampa. On its banks rises the great mountain Rishyamooka. In a cave lives Sugriva, son of Surya and king of the monkeys with his four companions. He will help you in your search for Sita."

The brothers left and on their way reached the hermitage of Shabari, an aged female ascetic. She told them that she had been waiting for them to come for many years and offered them fruits. She directed them to go to Lake Pampa and Kishkindha, where they would meet Sugriva, who would help them find Sita.

The two brothers were almost at the foot of Rishyamooka when Sugriva saw them arrive. Seeing their demeanour and the weapons they possessed, he grew suspicious. He asked his minister Hanuman to take the form of an ascetic and find out why they were there. In a flash, Hanuman stood in front of Rama and Lakshmana as an ascetic. "Who are you and why have you come here? You are dressed as ascetics but carry weapons." Rama was impressed with the way Hanuman had conducted himself and told Lakshmana to speak to him courteously. "We are Princes from Ayodhya. My brother's wife Sita has been abducted by the demon Ravana and we are moving in search of her. We are in fact looking for Sugriva."

Hanuman was satisfied with their response and said, "Sugriva, the king of the monkeys extends his hand of friendship. I am his minister, in the guise of a mendicant at his command. Assuming his true form, he lifted both the brothers on his shoulders and leaped across the lake to Sugriva. They spoke on the way and once they reached Sugriva, Hanuman told him about how Sita had been abducted. In the presence of Agni, the Fire God, both Rama and Sugriva swore mutual friendship forever. Sugriva then said, "My friend, we both share a common sorrow. My wife was taken away by Vali, my brother who has banished me from his kingdom." Both Rama and Sugriva decided to help each other.

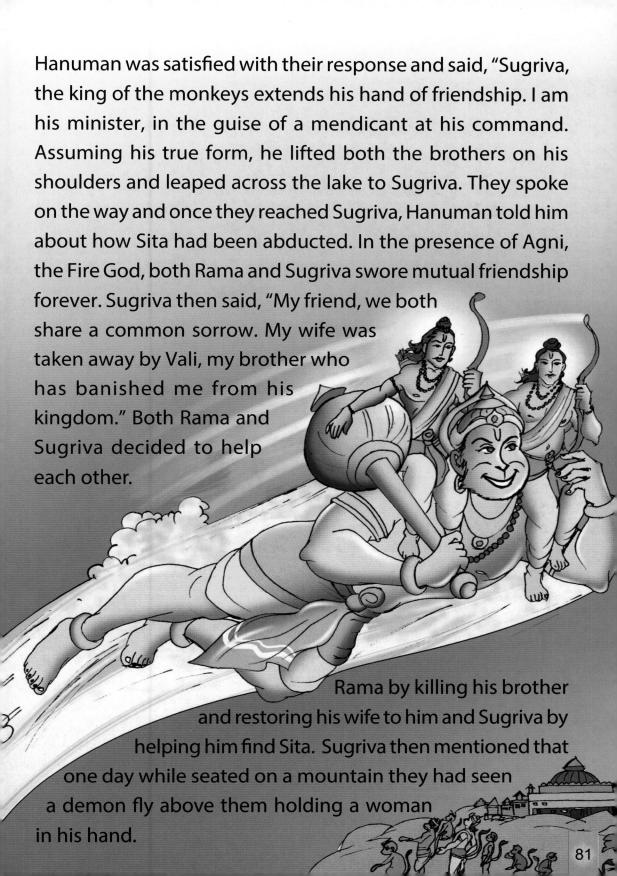

Rama by killing his brother and restoring his wife to him and Sugriva by helping him find Sita. Sugriva then mentioned that one day while seated on a mountain they had seen a demon fly above them holding a woman in his hand.

The woman had thrown some of her ornaments while crying out, "Rama, Lakshmana." Rama grew impatient and asked to see the jewels. He identified them to be of Sita's.

Sugriva then began to tell Rama about his banishment. "I served my elder brother Vali as he ruled the kingdom. One day, a demon named Manyavi picked up a fight with Vali over a woman and came to the palace to challenge Vali to a duel.

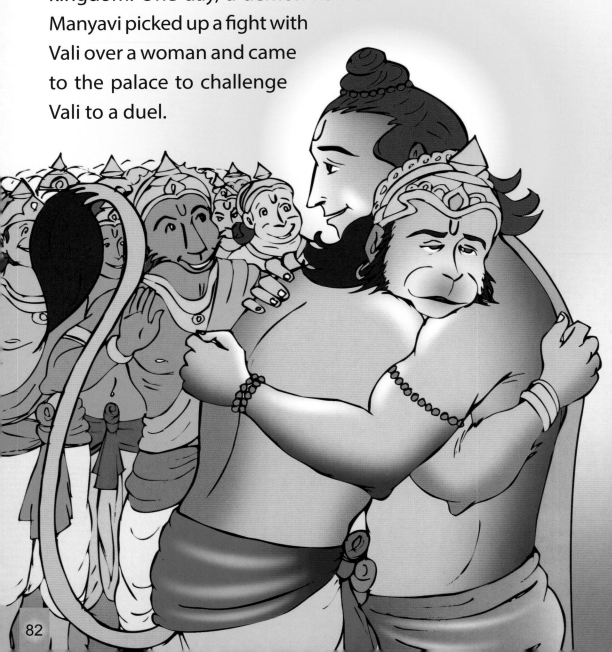

Although we all tried to dissuade him, he disagreed and went towards the forest and I followed him. We approached an underground cavern, where Vali went inside and told me to wait outside. I waited for an entire year. Suddenly I saw blood trickling out of the cave and yet no Vali. I realized that Manyavi had killed him and if Manyavi came out, he would have killed me too. So I took a boulder and blocked the entry to the cave. I returned to Kishkindha and informed everyone about Vali.

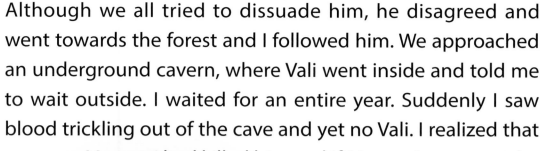

I was crowned the king and I was doing my duties when one day Vali returned, enraged that I had taken over the throne. He didn't even give me a chance to explain and banished me along with my followers from the kingdom."

Rama smiled at the thought of an easy victory but Sugriva warned him and told him of Vali's exploits. One day a demon called Dundubhi approached the gates of Kishkindha. Vali attacked him with his bare hands and catching him by his horns, flung him far away. The impact shattered his jaw, but the blood spread to Matanga's hermitage tarnishing it. Matanga then cursed Vali that if he or his kin enters the woods and area surrounding the Rishyamooka mountain, they would be turned to stone for years. And that is the reason why Sugriva chose to live there as Vali could not reach him.

The Monkey Army

Rama then suggested they should head towards Kishkindha so that Sugriva could challenge Vali to a duel. And once they began fighting, Rama hiding behind some bushes would aim his arrow and Vali would be killed. On reaching the gates of Kishkindha, Sugriva challenged Vali. But as they began to fight, Rama realized they looked like twins, he could not differentiate one from another and thus hesitated to attack.

Sugriva soon grew tired and wondered why Rama had not kept his word. He retreated from the fight and returned to Rishyamooka. There Rama told him why he had not killed his brother. He then placed a garland on him and convinced him to challenge his brother again and this time he would not miss. But this time Vali's wife Tara begged him not to fight, for she believed that Sugriva wouldn't dare challenge him twice if he didn't have someone's protection. Vali did not listen and went outside to kill Sugriva once and for all. But when the fight ensued, Rama shot an arrow which pierced Vali's chest and he fell to the ground.

Tara and Angada, Vali's wife and son rushed to his side. Vali then asked Sugriva to look after his son and not harm Tara for his misdeeds. Finally he gave the divine necklace that he wore, to Sugriva and breathed his last. After performing the last rites for Vali, Rama advised Sugriva to enter Kishkindha and perform his duties well, declaring Angada as the heir-apparent. "Lakshmana and I will spend the next four months in Mount Prasravana, and wait out the rainy season. We will begin our search for Sita when the monsoon ends." Saying this Rama and Lakshmana took their leave. Four long months passed and though the rains were over, Sugriva had not shown any signs of preparation for Sita's search. Hanuman urged him to do so quickly. Otherwise he would soon be at the receiving end of Rama's wrath. Sugriva then commanded Nila, the leader of the armies to gather all the monkeys in full strength within fifteen days. By this time, Rama had also become disgruntled with Sugriva for not having done anything.

He sent Lakshmana and asked him to convey his discontent and warn Sugriva of miseries that would come his way if he wavered from his promise. Sugriva who had been lying in a drunken state woke up hearing a loud sound. He sent for Hanuman who said alarmingly, "I had warned you that you should do something about your promise to Rama, but now Lakshmana has come to our gates angered that you have not kept to your word." Angada escorted Lakshmana to the palace where he met Tara, Sugriva's wife. She tried to subdue his anger and finally led him to Sugriva. Sugriva apologized for his mistake and begged for forgiveness. Lakshmana impressed with his humility said that it is necessary that plans proceed at the earliest for they were wasting time.

Sugriva ordered Hanuman to gather all the monkeys at once and accompanied by Lakshmana, Hanuman and an entire army of monkeys went to meet Rama. Sugriva gathered his army and explained the plan for Sita's search. He divided them into four divisions heading North, South, East and West appointing a commander for each and giving them one month to bring news of Sita or be put to death if they returned without any.

Rama then gave Hanuman his ring saying, "Once you show this ring to Sita, she will know that it is from me and will trust you and know that you are my messenger." Hanuman along with Angada, Nila, and Jambavan who was the veteran of the bears went towards the South.

Within a month, the divisions that had proceeded North, East and West returned empty handed and Sugriva waited in anticipation for the party from the South to return with some good news.

Sampati

What happened to my brother Jatayu?

Things were not looking up for Hanuman's group. They had searched through every terrain of the Vindhya mountains and found themselves on the shores of a vast ocean. They had no clue as to where to proceed from there. The monkeys sat in despair wondering what fate awaited them as they had failed and did not know where Sita was. They were demoralized and decided to fast to death. Angada felt that he would rather face death here, than face his stepfather Sugriva. Hanuman too wondered what they should do.

As they sat on the shores, above them two gleaming eyes were watching them from a nearby hill. They were of an old vulture that hadn't had a meal for many days. The bird was happy as its prey had literally walked into its mouth. But as soon as he was about to pounce, he heard Hanuman speaking of his brother Jatayu and how he had tried to protect Sita from the hands of Ravana. Hearing this, he asked, "Who speaks of my brother Jatayu? I have heard his name after so long only to hear of his death. Tell me how it happened. I am Sampati, his elder brother."

Sampati then asked them to help him down the cliff as his wings had been burnt and he could not fly. After helping him down, Angada told him about Sita's abduction, how Jatayu tried to save her and his fatal battle against Ravana. Sampati grew teary eyed and decided to help these monkeys. He told him that some months back he had seen a powerful demon carrying a woman in his chariot, who cried out, "Rama, Rama" as they flew overhead. That must have been Sita. Sampati being a descendent from Garuda, was blessed with a sixth sense. He also told them that Ravana had Sita captive under heavy guard in Lanka, a city situated on an island across the ocean, eight hundred miles away from where they stood. Hearing this, the monkeys were ecstatic. Once he gave this information to the monkeys, Sampati regained his wings. He had been given a boon that when he would help Rama and meet the monkeys, he would regain his wings and strength.

As they approached the shores, the monkeys discussed who could cross the ocean to give Sita the message that they would return with Rama. After all options ran out, Jambavan looked at Hanuman and urged him to go ahead, as he was but the son of Vayu, the God of Wind. He told him that he had been blessed at birth that no weapon could kill him and that he would die of his free will. Inspired by his words, Hanuman aroused his dormant strength and was soon headed towards Lanka.

Hanuman goes to Lanka

Hanuman had now assumed his full, gigantic form and seemed to fill the sky, while at the same time dwarfing the ocean. With one jump he reached the peak of a mountain. Within a minute he was airborne on his way to find Sita in Lanka.

The Mainaka Mountain rose from the middle of the sea, to provide a resting place for Hanuman. He thanked the mountain, but moved on as he was pressed for time. As he went a little further, Surasa, the mother of serpents blocked his path and opened her mouth, ready to devour him. "I have been granted a boon, that nobody should cross my mouth once it is opened," she said to Hanuman.

"Then open your mouth wider as I will not fit," replied Hanuman. When she opened her mouth wider, in a flash of a second, he shrank to a miniscule size, went quickly inside and came out again.

"I have fulfilled my obligation and have not broken your boon. So let me pass," said Hanuman to Surasa as he went ahead towards his destination.

Along his way, a demoness called Singhika captured him by taking hold of his vast shadow. As he was being pulled down, Hanuman entered the female demon's mouth and killed her by tearing open her stomach. He then continued his journey and reached Lanka. Nearing Lanka, he stood on the Trikuta Mountain, assessing the entire city. Changing his form to a small monkey which was no bigger than a cat, he decided to enter the city at night. As he entered the city, a fearsome demoness stopped him and rudely demanded, "Who are you and what do you seek?" Hanuman answered meekly, "I have heard so much about the city. I just want to look at its grandeur. But who are you and why are you so angry?" "I am Lanka, the spirit of the city in person and I guard it with my life. I cannot give you permission to wander around."

"I shall return as soon as I see the city," repeated Hanuman. Lanka lost her temper and attacked him. Hanuman, in response, grew to a huge size and struck her with his club. She looked at him in surprise, as she fell and got up as she was reminded of a prophecy.

"The hour has come. It had been destined that the day a monkey overpowers the spirit of Lanka, Ravana and his clan's end would be near." Saying this, she let Hanuman pass.

Entering the city, Hanuman saw the opulence with which it had been built by the celestial architect Vishwakarma. He looked through the whole city for Sita and then entered the palace where Ravana lay surrounded by beautiful women, one of whom Hanuman almost mistook for being Sita, only to realize that she would never sleep in the palace in the proximity of Ravana. As he exited the palace, thoughts of failure surrounded him. He could not go back empty handed.

walking towards the gardens, he decided to go to the one place he hadn't searched – Ravana's grove of ashoka trees.

Near the grove, he heard some sounds and climbed a tree. Peeping through the leaves he saw a lady in soiled clothing, weak and crying, surrounding her were a circle of fierce demonesses. Hanuman knew that this could only be Sita. He then waited for an opportune time to speak to her. Soon, he heard Ravana approach with his entourage to see Sita. Ravana stood before Sita. Seeing him, she began to tremble with fear. Ravana tried every possible way to win her over - through temptation, fear and even deceit, but Sita would not listen.

She belonged only to Rama. She threatened him that Rama would come and kill him and he should therefore beg for forgiveness till he had time. Ravana irked by her remarks said, "You have two months time left.

If you do not reconsider, you shall not live." As he left, the demonesses surrounding Sita began to tease and tempt her into becoming Ravana's wife.

Suddenly, a demoness named Trijata warned the others that she had dreamt that Rama had entered Lanka, killing Ravana and saw Lanka's end. "Do not trouble this woman, seek her forgiveness. Only then shall you survive."

All this while, Hanuman was listening perched in the tree. He thought that if he suddenly appeared before Sita she might mistake him to be a demon. Thus he remained in the tree and in a sweet, low voice started narrating tales of Rama. As soon as Sita heard the name of her dear Rama, she looked up only to see a small monkey.

Hanuman then climbed down the tree, and bowing before Sita gave her the ring given to him by Rama. Seeing the ring, Sita knew that help was on the way and that Rama would come to save her. She then gave him a jewel to give to Rama as a token of remembrance, and for Hanuman it was the proof of their having met.

Before going back, Hanuman decided to demonstrate his prowess to the enemies. Growing in size, he began by uprooting trees, crushing rocks, trampling around the grove and left no spot untouched except the tree under which Sita was sitting. The guards couldn't stop him and ran to Ravana telling him that a monkey was creating havoc in the groves. On hearing about Hanuman destroying the groves, Ravana ordered his bodyguards to catch him.

Singing praise for Rama, Lakshmana and Sugriva, Hanuman lifted a giant pillar and throwing it at the bodyguards, killed them in one blow. Ravana sent his bravest warriors to crush Hanuman only to be defeated by him. Finally Ravana sent his son, Indrajita to prove his valour against what could only seem like no ordinary monkey. After a long fight, Indrajita took out the weapon of Brahma and struck Hanuman, thereby immobilizing him. But this was Hanuman's plan as he knew the only way to reach Ravana's court was to be captured.

Brought before Ravana, Prahasta, his minister, questioned Hanuman. "Who are you and where have you come from? Who has sent you? Tell the truth and you shall be set free."

"I am a mere monkey," answered Hanuman, "but I wished to see Ravana so I destroyed the grove knowing that after my capture I would meet him. I come on behalf of Sugriva. If you do not let Sita go, then Rama along with an entire army of monkeys shall be at your gate." Ravana grew angrier and ordered Prahasta to kill Hanuman at once. Ravana's brother Vibhishana then advised him, "You should not kill a messenger. It is a great sin. You may put him through torture but you cannot kill him." Ravana agreed with his brother and ordered Hanuman's tail to be put on fire and ordered, "He should be humiliated and paraded through the streets of Lanka."

As he was paraded around, Hanuman gauged the entire city of Lanka and once he grew tired of roaming the streets, he shrank to a miniscule size and loosened his ropes. Then growing back in size, he began to jump from one roof top to another burning building after building with his tail. In a little while the entire city was ablaze.

On completing his work, Hanuman dipped his burning tail into the ocean only to question whether Sita was safe or not? He then rushed to the 'Ashoka Vatika' and seeing that it had not been harmed, he took Sita's blessings and returned with good news to his monkey companions.

Rama Approaches Lanka

Approaching the other side of the ocean, Hanuman let out a loud roar. After descending from his flight, he narrated the entire story of his journey to his monkey army. Then they proceeded to tell Rama, Lakshmana and Sugriva the good news.

On their way, the monkeys celebrated and hearing their cries of celebration, Sugriva's curiosity arose. On the monkeys arrival, Hanuman touched Rama's feet, gave him the ornament Sita had given him and assured Rama of her being safe and unharmed. Then the entire story of Hanuman's exploits was related to all. Rama spoke to Hanuman and on assessing the kingdom's strength and weaknesses, told Sugriva to inform the monkey army to move forward. He also declared that when the time comes, they would decide how to cross the ocean. After a long journey, the army of monkeys along with Rama, Lakshmana, Hanuman and Sugriva reached a forest near the vast ocean and camped there for the night.

During this time, Ravana too was busy preparing a plan to overthrow Rama. Lanka's morale was low, but the ministers and the warriors encouraged Ravana towards victory. Ravana's brother Kumbhakarna differed from the others. He had awoken from his six month sleep and was angered by his brother's decision of not having consulted him before abducting Sita. He nevertheless showed his support towards protecting Lanka. Ravana's younger brother Vibhishana tried to persuade him not to go to war and return Sita back to Rama. Ravana yet again declined his advice and told him to leave the kingdom.

Along with his four followers, Vibhishana mounted a flying chariot and went to seek Rama's protection. As they approached, the monkeys became wary of their intentions. But after a lot of debate and consulting Rama, they allowed Vibhishana to meet him. He then clarified his position and sought Rama's refuge. He also told them about Ravana's boon which ensured that he could not be killed by any God, demon, or semi-divine creatures along with details about his entire army. Soon, he became a part of Rama's legion. While Hanuman and Sugriva deliberated on how to cross the ocean, Vibhishana suggested that Rama should pray to the ocean to let the army pass, as the ocean was created by King Sagara of the Ikshvakus, who would be bound to oblige his descendant Rama.

Rama sat to pray, but after three days there were no results. Rama grew irritated and drew his bow so that he could dry up the ocean. The Ocean King suddenly appeared and asked Rama to retract his bow. But as Rama had already drawn his bow, the Ocean King requested him to kill a tribe that had been polluting its waters. As soon as Rama had done this, the Ocean King descended after declaring, "Nala, from the army of monkeys is the son of Vishwakarma, the divine architect. Under his guidance you will be able to find a way to cross my waters."

For five days, five thousand monkeys under Nala's instructions using rocks, hills and trees built a bridge to Lanka. While the monkeys were building the bridge, a tiny squirrel watched them from a nearby tree. She also came down, and taking small particles of sand, released it over the bridge. She continued this for days, oblivious to hunger and thirst. This was the most sincere contribution of a small animal for the noble cause. And thus, in order to thank her, Rama stroked her back. It is believed that the three dark lines which appear on a squirrel's back are due to Rama's blessings.

The army crossed the ocean via foot, air and water while Rama and Lakshmana mounted Hanuman and Angada respectively. Reaching Lanka, they set up camp and let go of Shuka, a demon disguised as a parrot, who had earlier tried to convince Sugriva to back out.

The Battle Begins

Shuka hurried to Ravana announcing the arrival of Rama in Lanka. Ravana then sent Shuka back along with Sarana, disguised as monkeys to gauge the strength of Rama's army. They were soon caught, and returned with Rama's message. "Tomorrow, Ravana shall taste my strength and he should summon up that same courage with which he carried Sita away. For tomorrow he will witness the destruction of Lanka and his army."

Ravana grew pensive on hearing the message but refused to give up. He decided that the only way this could be solved was if Sita agreed to marry him.

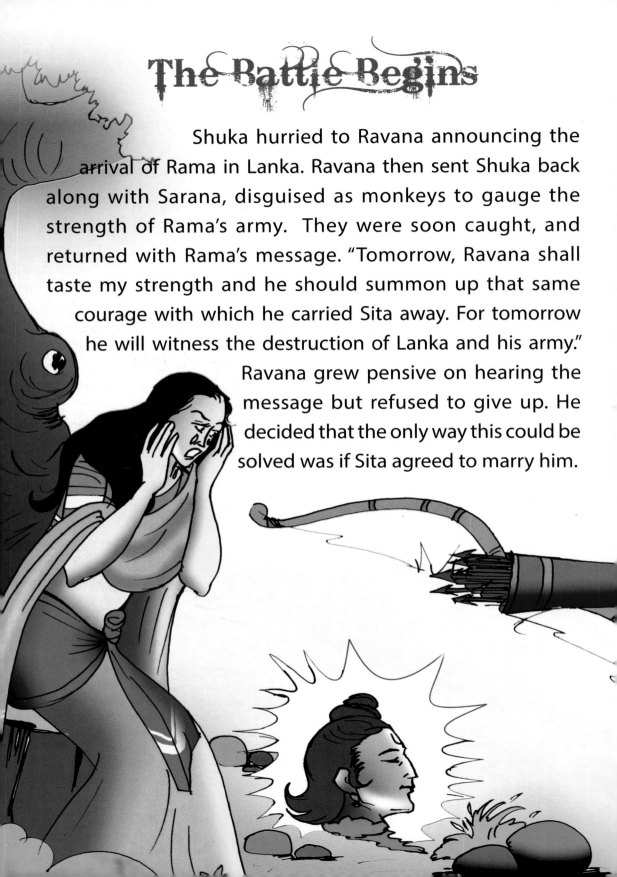

He then sent for one of his demons, skilled in creating hallucinations and produced two things - the head of Rama and his bow and arrows. He went to show these to Sita. She was mortified, but after Ravana left, was consoled by one of the guards called Sarama who said that Rama was still alive and war was imminent. Ravana gathered his counsellors together for their final consultation, where his maternal grandfather, Malyavan suggested that he should make peace with Rama, or face his end. Ravana did not pay heed to his advice and continued on his warpath.

Your Rama is dead!

At break of day, Rama and his army faced Lanka and saw Ravana on his terrace dressed in scarlet robes. Seeing him, Sugriva indifferent to consequences, in one bounding leap stood before Ravana and attacked him savagely. They fought till Ravana showed signs of exhaustion, and Sugriva flew back. When he returned Rama rebuked him for not having consulted him before he acted and said, "Killing Ravana and rescuing Sita are to only be my tasks."

Angada was then sent as a messenger to Ravana forewarning him about his fate. "Kill him," Ravana ordered his guards on seeing Angada. But Angada was stronger and leapt into the air and reached Rama. By then the monkey army had been let loose and Lanka was under heavy siege. The monkeys used weapons like trees, rocks, stones, tooth and claw to fight off the demons. Rama was attacked by four demons simultaneously and then six more. He killed them all with his skill and speed.

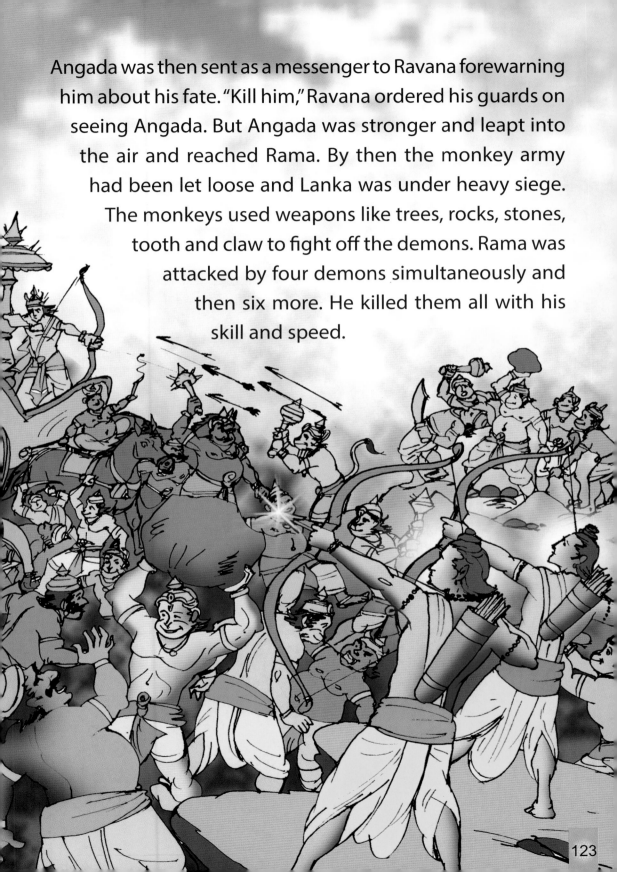

On the other front, Angada had taken on Indrajita and had smashed his chariot while killing his horses. Indrajita was exhausted but with his God given powers, became invisible. Angada thought that he had retreated, but Indrajita began attacking Rama and Lakshmana with his magical weapons and soon had entrapped them with an arrow charged with a serpent spell with which both were unable to move and fell to the ground.

Indrajita then went to Ravana and told him the good news. Hearing this news, Ravana told a demon woman to take his aerial chariot Pushpaka and show Sita their corpses.

The monkeys had by then gathered around Rama and Lakshmana and began to grieve. Vibhishana told Sugriva to tell his army not to lose faith, as the brothers were not dead, but unconscious and they should guard their bodies so that no harm comes to them. This word was spread through the troops making sure that their morale didn't shatter.

Sita was now in the chariot with the demoness Trijata, and broke down while sobbing hysterically on seeing their bodies. Trijata convinced her that they were not dead, only unconscious. Sita was hurt and deeply disturbed but alas! She could not do anything.

Garuda

After some time, Rama regained consciousness only to see his brother lying next to him. Shocked that his brother had died, Rama asked the army to retreat, but soon became unconscious again. It was a grave crisis. Suddenly, Garuda, the mighty eagle, who is Lord Vishnu's vehicle, landed.

Coming closer to Rama and Lakshmana, he stroked their bodies by which the serpent power that bound the two brothers began to loosen and soon enough their bodies were devoid of any scars. Rama asked this great creature, "Who are you?"

"I am your friend and once you rescue Sita and return victorious to Ayodhya, you will know who I am." Saying this Garuda flew into the sky. Presuming that Rama and Lakshmana were dead, Ravana was surprised to hear the jubilant roar of the monkeys.

The monkeys had in fact found out that Rama was alive and safe. The minute his messenger arrived with the news of both brothers being alive, Ravana sent his general, Dhumraksha to kill Rama. As Dhumraksha set out in his golden chariot, Hanuman obstructed his path and attacked him. A battle followed, where Hanuman vanquished Dhumraksha. One by one, Ravana sent forth his strongest demons but in vain for Vajradanshtra was slain by Angada; Akampana was killed by Hanuman and then came Prahasta, who was eventually killed by Nila.

Seeing his entire demon ranks defeated, Ravana himself turned to battle. The ten-headed demon approached Rama rising like a mountain of fury. The first to confront Ravana was Sugriva, who rushed at him with a mountain peak and hurled it at him with great force but Ravana's shower of golden arrows broke it into pieces. He then chose a serpent arrow and aimed it at Sugriva, wounding him. After Sugriva, Nila began to attack him. He shrank in size and moved all along Ravana's body, irritating him. But soon he too became a victim to Ravana's arrow and collapsed.

Suddenly, Ravana turned around only to find Lakshmana standing in front of him. It was a raging but equal battle in terms of strength, but soon Ravana hurled his deadliest weapon at Lakshmana, wounding him as he fell down. Seeing this Hanuman charged at Ravana and struck him on his chest. Ravana fell a few feet away and was shaken up. Hanuman lifted Lakshmana and took him to the safety of his brother. Rama had now reached the spot where Ravana stood, exhausted after the last blow by Hanuman. Rama shattered his chariot, his arrows, his bows and his glittering crown and told him to come back the next day after taking rest, for he would not fight him as he was exhausted but only when he had regained his vigour and strength. "Come back tomorrow refreshed with a new chariot and weapons and then we shall fight," declared Rama to Ravana. Ashamed, Ravana returned to his palace.

kumbhakarna

Ravana now knew that it was almost impossible to defeat Rama. He asked his ministers to rouse his brother Kumbhakarna from his sleep. Kumbhakarna had been cursed that if he would go to sleep, he would remain in that state for six months at a stretch. Therefore it wasn't an easy task to wake him. Ravana's ministers arranged for Kumbhakarna's meals and made great efforts to rouse him by blowing conches, beating drums, and finally making elephants walk over his body. He was eventually stirred and as he awoke one of the ministers told him about the situation in Lanka and that his brother beckoned him.

Kumbhakarna reminded Ravana of his advice, but Ravana asked that he should forget the past and save Lanka from Rama and his army. Adorned with ornaments Kumbhakarna went to battle with his spear.

As Kumbhakarna walked the streets, he devoured any monkey which came in his way. Hanuman only managed to break his spear and soon, he fought against Sugriva and rendering him unconscious went back to Ravana. But their joy was short-lived. The moment Sugriva regained consciousness, he attacked Kumbhakarna tearing his nose and ears and then flew back to Rama.

133

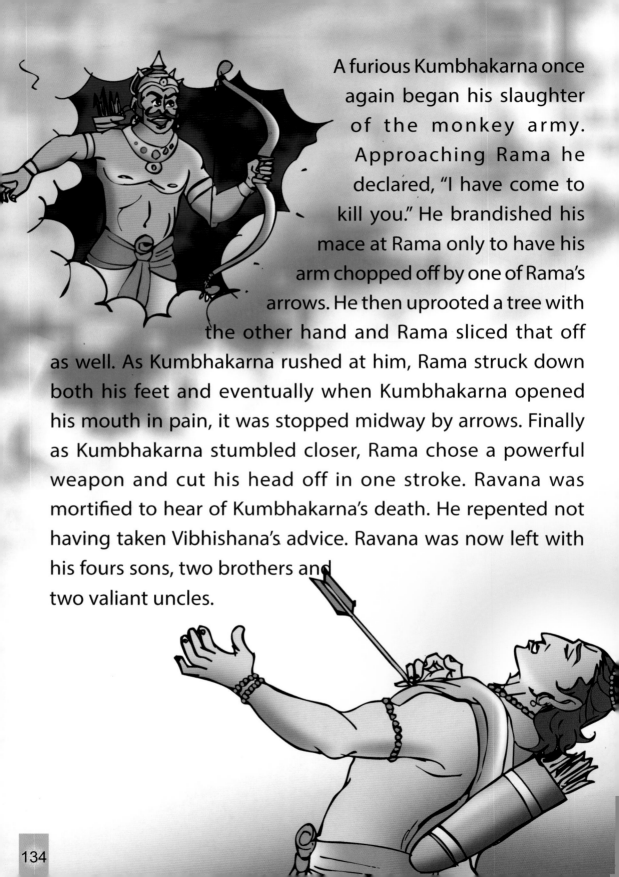

A furious Kumbhakarna once again began his slaughter of the monkey army. Approaching Rama he declared, "I have come to kill you." He brandished his mace at Rama only to have his arm chopped off by one of Rama's arrows. He then uprooted a tree with the other hand and Rama sliced that off as well. As Kumbhakarna rushed at him, Rama struck down both his feet and eventually when Kumbhakarna opened his mouth in pain, it was stopped midway by arrows. Finally as Kumbhakarna stumbled closer, Rama chose a powerful weapon and cut his head off in one stroke. Ravana was mortified to hear of Kumbhakarna's death. He repented not having taken Vibhishana's advice. Ravana was now left with his fours sons, two brothers and two valiant uncles.

But when they entered battle, they were defeated by Angada, Hanuman and Lakshmana. Hearing about the death of his sons and uncles, Ravana realized the true potential of Rama and his army. His son Indrajita then consoled him saying that he would strike both Rama and Lakshmana and bring his father good news. Indrajita then prayed to Lord Brahma and gathering his special power of invisibility, started raiding the monkey army, severely injuring many of the monkey leaders. Using the weapon of Brahma, Indrajita attacked Lakshmana and rendered him unconscious. The monkeys began to panic in confusion but Vibhishana and Hanuman gathered them to tell them the brothers were still alive and tried to preserve their morale and enthusiasm.

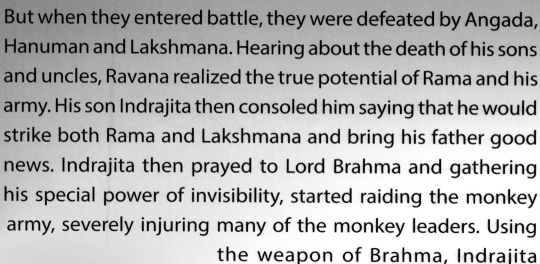

Hanuman was looking for Jambavan, Vibhishana found him weakened by loss of blood as he was hurt. Jambavan said to Hanuman, "Rush to the Himalayas, between Mount Kailasa and Mount Rishabha, there stands a splendid mountain of medicinal herbs. You must look for four glowing plants, for only they will revive Lakshmana." Within a second, Hanuman was airborne headed towards the mountains.

When he reached, the plants stopped glowing as they knew he had come to take them. Not knowing what to do, Hanuman picked up the entire mountain and returned. As Hanuman landed, the fragrance of the aromatic medicinal herbs spread, healing the monkeys, the wounded and the dead.

Lakshmana too opened his eyes to the welcome sight of the entire army stronger than before. As for the dead demons, they were not affected as they had been thrown into the ocean.

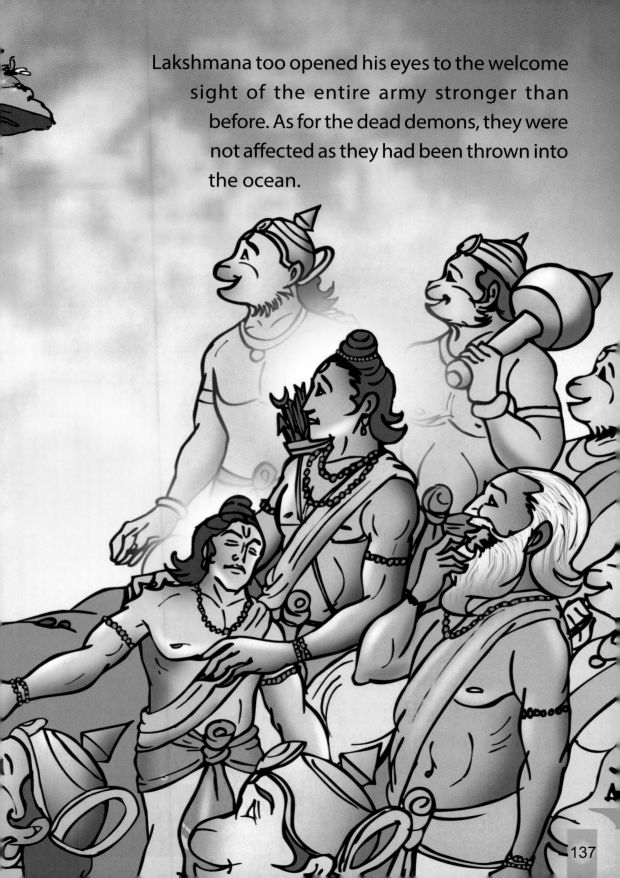

Sugriva consulted Hanuman and decided that Ravana would no longer come out alone to battle and that this was the opportune time to strike at Lanka. As the city was set on fire, the remaining leaders of the demon clan were killed. Ravana once again sent for Indrajita, who attacked veiled in smoke. Indrajita used his illusory powers to create a hallucination of Sita and holding her by her hair, paraded her around in his chariot.

Seeing him, Hanuman shouted, "You dare lift a finger on Sita, you will surely die at the hands of Rama." Indrajita scoffed and replied, "I will kill her for she has caused enough trouble. Then I will kill Rama, Lakshmana, Sugriva, Vibhishana and you." Saying this he cut off her head.

Hearing about Sita's death, Rama fainted but was assured by Vibhishana that this was one of Indrajita's tricks as he needed time to perform a sacrifice to the Goddess Nikumbhila which would bring him invincibility when he completes it. Vibhishana along with Lakshmana proceeded to find Indrajita. Lakshmana stopped the ritual and Indrajita was thus forced to fight with him, but having left the ritual mid way Indrajita no longer had the power of invisibility. Lakshmana soon broke his chariot and killed his horse. A long and tireless battle ensued but Lakshmana emerged victorious and Indrajita was killed.

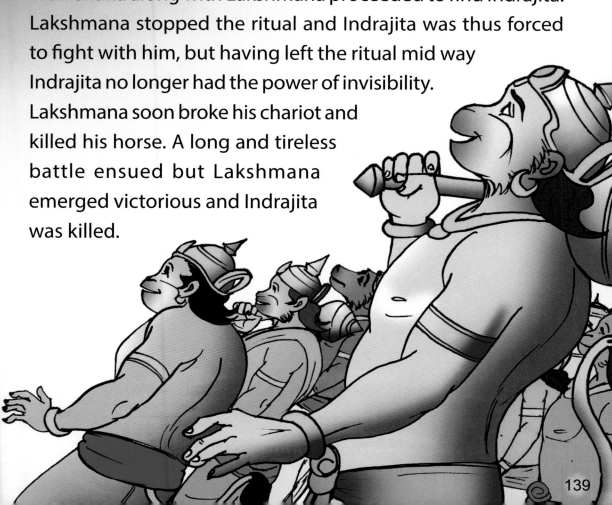

Shaken by Indrajita's death, Ravana began to lose his temper and wanted to avenge his death. He was so enraged that he decided to kill Sita first as she was the cause of everything. Ravana's counsellor asked him not to kill a woman for it was a sin. He heeded to his counsellor and returned only to command his remaining ministers to go to battle with him for he had enough and was thirsty for Rama's blood.

The Final Battle

Ravana entered the battle with the last of his demon army and began their killing spree. Both sides fought each other for a number of days until Ravana saw many strong and brave demon soldiers being killed in front of his eyes. His only aim now was to destroy Rama and Lakshmana. Lakshmana tried to stop Ravana's assault with a volley of arrows. In retaliation, Ravana aimed a weapon of pure energy at Lakshmana hitting him. Lakshmana fell. Rama began to attack Ravana but felt his power ebb as his brother was not beside him. Hanuman was then told to bring the herbs that he had earlier brought to revive Lakshmana. The herbs had their affect, and Lakshmana arose full of life.

The Gods who were witnessing the battle realized that Rama needed help as he fought on foot while Ravana was riding his chariot. Lord Indra then offered not only his chariot but his charioteer Matali to Rama.

Rama ascended the golden chariot of Indra and the fight continued. As Rama and Ravana clashed, Rama was surprised to see that whenever he struck one of Ravana's heads, another one would replace it. The whole process seemed futile. Rama then finally drew his bow, aimed at Ravana's navel and released the weapon of Brahma. The arrow pierced Ravana's heart, hit the earth and returned to its quiver. Ravana fell from his chariot and breathed his last.

News of Ravana's death spread through Lanka like wild fire. His wives soon came out wailing. Queen Mandodari, Ravana's favourite addressed his body saying, "I warned you to return Sita but your passion for her destroyed our entire city and killed you as well." Vibhishana then led her away and returned to Lanka to perform the funeral rites of Ravana.

Vibhishana was then declared the King of Lanka after a small coronation ceremony.

Fire Test

Rama then sent Hanuman to tell Sita about the good news. She was elated and wanted to see Rama. But Sita was to come to Rama once she had bathed, perfumed and adorned herself. She arrived in a palanquin and it stopped a little away from Rama. Rama told her to come to him on foot. She hesitantly walked towards him perturbed by his demeanour.

Rama then spoke in a serious tone, "I have won you back and avenged the wrong done to you. Hanuman, Sugriva and Vibhishana were with me throughout." Sita looked at him in confusion as he continued, "Doubts have been cast on your purity and I cannot disregard that. I will have nothing to do with you. You are free to go where you wish with whom you wish. We no longer share any bond."

Sita was shocked. Rama had rejected her and that too in front of so many people. She wept, hurt by Rama's words and replied, "Ravana had seized me by force and I did not consent to it.

My heart is yours and remains untouched. Yet you hesitate to accept me?" She then told Lakshmana to kindle a fire for she no longer wished to live having been falsely charged by her own husband. Lakshmana looked angrily at Rama but obeyed Sita. Sita then walked around the fire, praying to Agni, the God of fire, "O Lord Agni, you know that I am pure and only Rama lies in my thoughts. Protect me!" Sita then fearlessly walked into the flames.

As Sita was engulfed in the flames, the Gods appeared from heaven and told Rama that he was the incarnation of Vishnu and Sita was Lakshmi and urged him to accept Sita. Suddenly, out of the fire rose Agni himself, carrying Sita in his arms. Presenting Sita to Rama he said, "Accept your wife Rama, she is pure!" The Gods showered flowers on Rama and Sita. With the help of Lord Indra's boon all the monkeys that had been killed in battle were brought to life. Rama, Sita, Lakshmana, Sugriva, Vibhishana, Hanuman and others then ascended the aerial chariot called Pushpaka and headed to Ayodhya.

Return to Ayodhya

On their way Rama showed Sita the various places, right from Panchavati to Lanka which he and Lakshmana had visited in search for her, giving her an account of their experiences and the people and demons they encountered. Rama landed in Bharadwaja's ashram and from there he sent Hanuman to inquire about Bharata and tell him about Rama's arrival. On hearing the news, Bharata was overjoyed. He welcomed Hanuman and bestowed him with gifts as he brought good news. He then began preparations in Nandigrama for Rama's arrival. He also informed Shatrughna to get Ayodhya ready to receive Rama with fervour. As Rama arrived in Nandigrama Bharata embraced his brother, and bent down reverently and placed Rama's feet in his sandals saying, "I now return your kingdom back to you. By your grace the kingdom has prospered hrough these years."

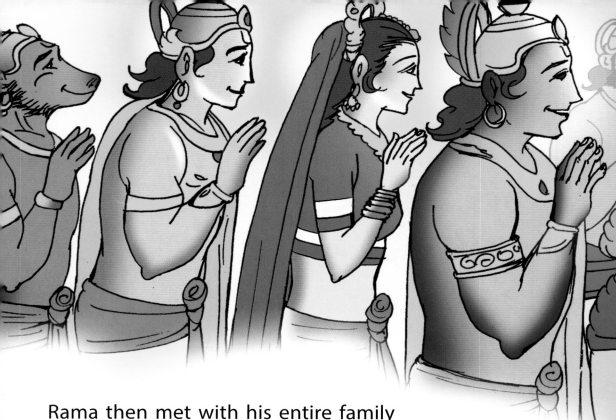

Rama then met with his entire family
and told them about Hanuman, Sugriva and Vibhishana and
how they had helped him. The procession from Nandigrama
moved to Ayodhya and the next day the coronation ceremony
was performed. A few months passed and all the guests left,
except for Hanuman. Hanuman was the greatest devotee of
Lord Rama and he wanted to spend the rest of his life serving
Lord Rama. Sugriva had felt bad that Hanuman had switched
loyalties and taunted him. To prove his sincere devotion to
Rama, Hanuman tore off his chest with his nails and lo! Sugriva
could not believe what he saw! An image of Rama and Sita
adorned the throne of Hanuman's heart. Sugriva understood
what Hanuman wanted to convey and immediately freed him
from all bonds.

The kingdom of Ayodhya was content and prosperous. Sita was soon pregnant and Rama and Sita should have lived happily for the rest of their days but destiny had other plans for them.

Sita's Rejection

One day, Rama, being in disguise, was walking through the streets of Ayodhya observing the lives of his subjects.

He suddenly saw a woman being turned out of her house by her husband. The man had grabbed her arms and was pushing her roughly, saying, "Why were you visiting that person's house alone? There is no place for a woman of loose character in my house. I abandon you as my wife." The woman replied, weeping, "Even King Rama did not abandon his wife even though she lived for several months in the palace of that evil *rakshasa* Ravana. All I did was visit the house of a relative."

Then she further added with bitter irony, "I suppose you think you are better than King Rama, with even stricter moral standards!" This incident had a profound impact on Rama.

In his heart, Rama knew that Sita was chaste and pure. But being the king and the moral head of his kingdom, he could not run the risk of gossip and scandal. He was duty bound to follow the rules. Finally, with a heavy heart, he decided to banish Sita. Lakshmana was given the sad task of leaving Sita in the forest.

Sita found herself wandering through the forest again, but this time without Rama or Lakshmana to protect her. She reached the hermitage of Sage Valmiki. The great sage was sympathetic towards her. Through his great power of meditation, he knew that Sita was pure and had been wrongly banished by Rama. Valmiki's hermitage became Sita's home and soon afterwards she gave birth to a healthy son. The baby was named Lava. Sita lived on with her baby in the safety of the hermitage; deprived of her husband but no longer forced to wander in the wild.

Lava Kusa

Sita doted on Lava, her baby son, but such was the safety of the hermitage that she usually left him unattended while she went to bathe.

So, one day, when Valmiki looked into her room and saw that Lava was not there, he was immediately worried that the baby had been carried off somehow.

Maybe a wild beast had got into the hermitage after all. Sita would be out of her mind with worry if she returned and found Lava missing. What should he do? Using his unique powers and skill, Valmiki made an exact replica of Lava out of *kusa* grass and placed him where Lava normally lay.

He hoped that Sita would think the replica was her own baby, and would therefore miss nothing. But soon afterwards Sita returned from her bath carrying Lava with her. She looked with amazement at the copy of her child, lying in a corner of her room, and said, 'I had Lava with me all the time, and now it seems I have a second baby who looks just like him. How can this be?" Valmiki explained why he had made the child.

"And because I made him out of kusa grass," he said, "let him be called Kusa, and be brought up as Lava's brother."

When they were older, Sita asked the *rishi* to school them on the Vedas, martial arts, archery, singing and music. He taught them well. During this time, Valmiki composed a poem called the Ramayana which, too, the boys learned to sing beautifully.

One day, they heard that the great King Rama of Ayodhya was planning to perform an Ashvamedha Yagna, a horse ceremony. Wherever the horse would go that land would become part of Rama's kingdom. If the people of that territory would not accept the king as their emperor, they would have to battle his mighty army. Lava and Kusa decided they would fight, and as the horse passed by their *ashram*, they captured it. A fierce battle followed in which many of the king's men were killed.

Rama then sent Lakshmana to the battlefield, but he returned, wounded.

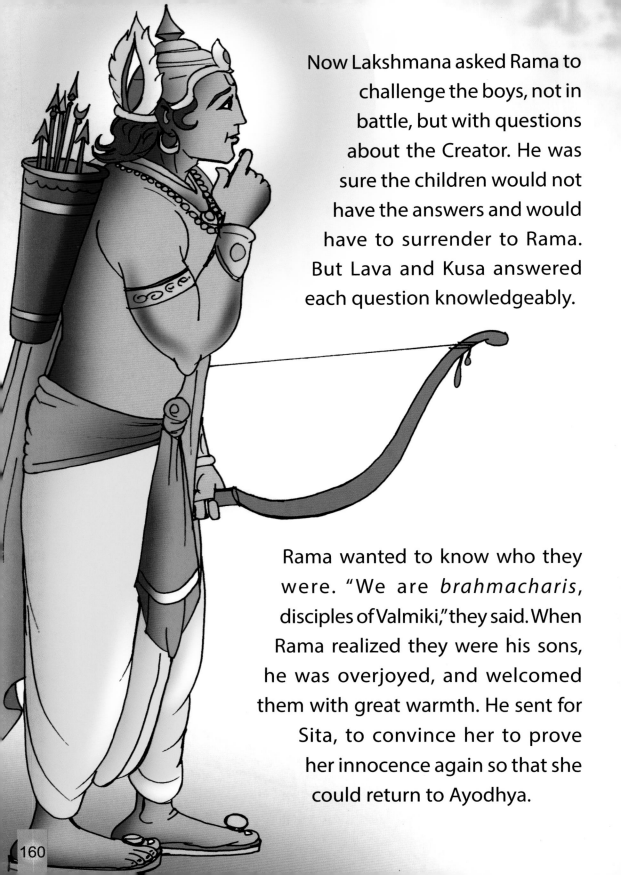

Now Lakshmana asked Rama to challenge the boys, not in battle, but with questions about the Creator. He was sure the children would not have the answers and would have to surrender to Rama. But Lava and Kusa answered each question knowledgeably.

Rama wanted to know who they were. "We are *brahmacharis*, disciples of Valmiki," they said. When Rama realized they were his sons, he was overjoyed, and welcomed them with great warmth. He sent for Sita, to convince her to prove her innocence again so that she could return to Ayodhya.

Sita arrived dressed in crimson and gold and Rama was delighted to see her. But Sita had grown tired of her difficult life. She prayed to Mother Earth to accept her in her fold so that she could be at peace for a while.

She said to Rama, "I will prove my purity before everyone for the last time." Then turning away, she continued, "Mother Earth, if I have been pure and have only had Rama in my heart, engulf me and take me with you."

With a great rumbling, the ground opened, took Sita in, and then closed over her.

Rama was shattered. He threatened to rip open the earth and reclaim Sita. But Brahma restrained him and said that he would join her only when his time would come. He also said that Rama should hear the end of the epic Ramayana from Lava and Kusa as they would recite it the next day and through it he would get his answers. After hearing the concluding portion of the epic, he realized that he would have to live out the rest of his days and he did so by keeping a golden image of Sita by his side. During the time Rama ruled in Ayodhya a whole new generation of Raghus arrived as Lakshmana, Shatrughna and Bharata's wives bore sons who eventually occupied their own cities in different regions. Rama's days on earth were numbered. The spirit of time and death in guise of an ascetic stood at the gates of his palace. Having been ushered in, Rama told Lakshmana that they were not to be disturbed. The ascetic said to Rama, "Your task is done and you have ruled for eleven thousand years. It is now time for you to return to your rightful position as Lord Vishnu in the heavens."

They were then interrupted by Lakshmana as Sage Durvasa had come to see Rama and this Sage's temper was not to be meddled with. But Rama remembered what the ascetic had said to him. "You will have to kill the one that disturbs us." Lakshmana had let the sage enter and thereby disturbed them.

Rama knew that he had to honour what the ascetic had said and called his advisors to suggest an alternate route. They suggested that Lakshmana should be banished rather than be killed.

Lakshmana withdrew from the kingdom and walked towards the river Sarayu. He then held his breath till he was finally in heaven having left his body on earth.

Rama's heart and spirit were broken as he did not have his brother or his wife by his side. He bid farewell to all who had helped and served him. Like his brother, he too went to the river Sarayu and walked into it. He was welcomed by Brahma and absorbed his natural form of Vishnu.

Lava and Kusa, the new kings of Ayodhya, traveled throughout India singing the Ramayana, Valmiki's glorious poem about their father. They would say, "Those who hear the Ramayana will learn about love, wisdom, and strength. They will be free of sins and live a long life."